THE BEA...

Specially arranged by *Cyril Ornadel* for the chromatic harmonica.

HARMONICA

Twenty-one classic Lennon/McCartney compositions.

SONGBOOK

Wise Publications
London/New York/Paris/Sydney/Copenhagen/Madrid

Exclusive Distributors:
Music Sales Limited
14/15 Berners Street,
London W1T 3LJ, England.
Music Sales Pty Limited
20 Resolution Drive
Caringbah, NSW 2229,
Australia.

Order No.NO90549
ISBN 0 7119 3323 5
This book © Copyright 1993 by Wise Publications

Music arranged by Cyril Ornadel
Music processed by Seton Music Graphics

Printed in the United Kingdom by
Caligraving Limited, Thetford, Norfolk.

Your Guarantee of Quality
As publishers, we strive to produce every book to the highest
commercial standards. The music has been freshly engraved and the book has been carefully
designed to minimise awkward page turns and to make playing from it a real pleasure.
Throughout, the printing and binding have been planned to ensure
a sturdy, attractive publication which should give years of enjoyment.
If your copy fails to meet our high standards, please
inform us and we will gladly replace it.

Music Sales' complete catalogue lists thousands of titles and is
free from your local music shop, or direct from Music Sales Limited.
Please send a cheque/postal order for £1.50 for postage to: Music Sales Limited,
Newmarket Road, Bury St. Edmunds, Suffolk IP33 3YB.

Cover photograph supplied by V & A Picture Library

This book is designed for the Chromatic Harmonica.

The numbers below the words tell you which hole to play.

The arrows pointing up ↑ mean *blow out.*

The arrows pointing down ↓ mean *draw (breath) in.*

The arrows pointing up and to the left ↰ mean blow out, *whilst pushing in the chromatic slide.*

The arrows pointing down and to the left ↲ mean draw (breath) in, *whilst pushing in the chromatic slide.*

All My Loving

Words & Music by John Lennon & Paul McCartney

Brightly

Gm · C7 · F · Dm

Close your eyes and I'll kiss you, To - mor - row I'll miss you; Re -
7 7 7 7 7 8 9 10 10 10 10 9 7 9

Bb · Gm · Eb · Gm

mem - ber I'll al - ways be true. ___ And then while I'm a -
9 9 8 7 7 6 7 7 7 7 7 7

C7 · F · Dm · Bb · C7

way, I'll write home ev' - ry day, ___ And I'll send all my lov - ing to
8 9 10 10 10 10 9 7 9 9 9 8 7 7 7

F · Gm · C7 · F

you. ___ I'll pre - tend that I'm kiss - ing, The lips I am
6 7 7 7 7 7 8 9 10 10 10 10

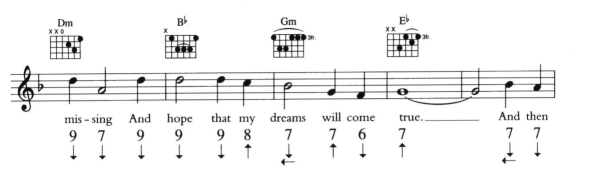

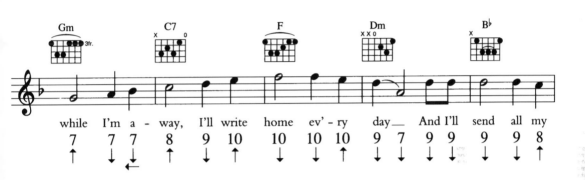

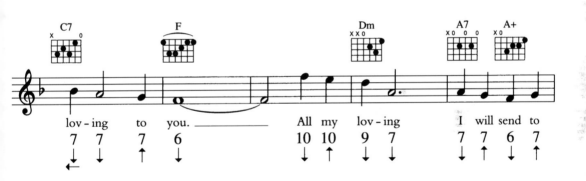

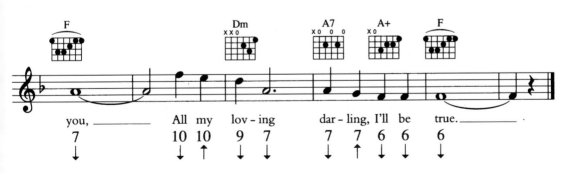

I Wanna Be Your Man

Words & Music by John Lennon & Paul McCartney

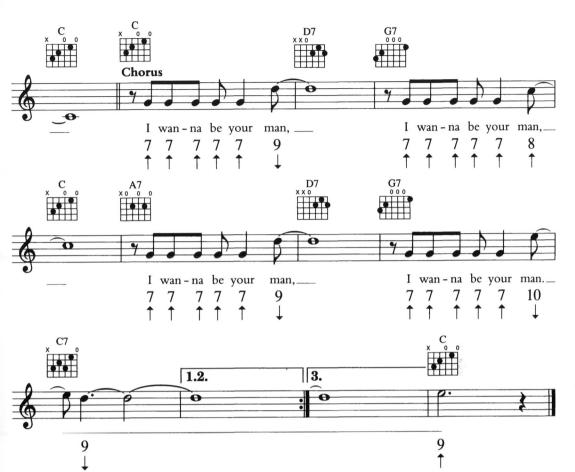

Chorus

I wan-na be your man, ____
7 7 7 7 7 9
↑ ↑ ↑ ↑ ↑ ↓

I wan-na be your man, ____
7 7 7 7 7 8
↑ ↑ ↑ ↑ ↑ ↑

I wan-na be your man, ____
7 7 7 7 7 9
↑ ↑ ↑ ↑ ↑ ↓

I wan-na be your man. ____
7 7 7 7 7 10
↑ ↑ ↑ ↑ ↑ ↓

1.2. **3.**

9
↓

9
↑

2. Tell me that you love me, babe,
Tell me you understand.
Tell me that you love me, babe,
I wanna be your man.
I wanna be your lover, babe,
I wanna be your man.
I wanna be your lover, babe,
I wanna be your man. I wanna be your man,
I wanna be your man, I wanna be your man,
I wanna be your man.

3. I wanna be your lover, babe,
I wanna be your man.
I wanna be your lover, babe,
I wanna be your man.
Love you like no other, babe,
Like no other can.
Love you like no other, babe,
Like no other can.
I wanna be your man, I wanna be your man,
I wanna be your man, I wanna be your man.

Let It Be

Words & Music by John Lennon & Paul McCartney

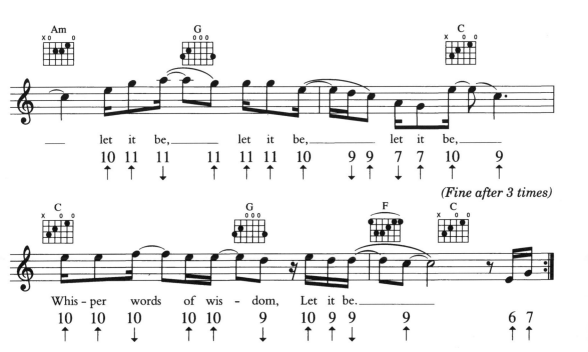

let it be,_____ let it be,_____ let it be,_____

10 11 11   11 11 11 10   9 9 7 7 10   9
↑ ↑ ↓   ↑ ↑ ↑ ↑   ↓ ↑ ↓ ↑ ↑   ↑

(Fine after 3 times)

Whis - per words of wis - dom, Let it be._____

10 10 10   10 10 9   10 9 9   9   6 7
↑ ↑ ↓   ↑ ↑ ↓   ↑ ↑ ↓   ↑   ↑ ↑

2.   And when the broken hearted people living in the world agree
There will be an answer. Let it be.
For though they may be parted, There is still a chance that they will see
There will be an answer, Let it be.
Let it be, let it be, let it be, let it be, There will be an answer,
Let it be.

3.   And when the night is cloudy There is still a light that shines on me
Shine until tomorrow, let it be.
I wake up to the sound of music, Mother Mary comes to me
Speaking words of wisdom, Let it be.
Let it be, let it be, let it be, let it be, whisper words of wisdom,
let it be.

I Want To Hold Your Hand

Words & Music by John Lennon & Paul McCartney

Day Tripper

Words & Music by John Lennon & Paul McCartney

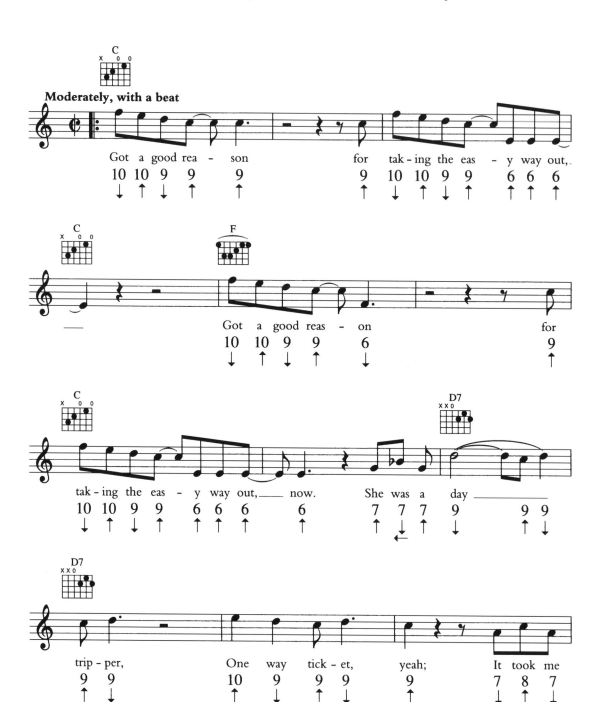

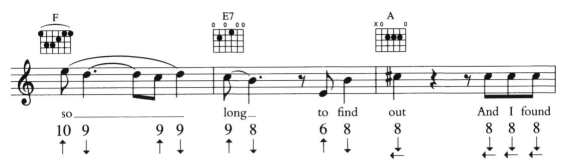

2. She's a big teaser, She took me half the way there.
   She's a big teaser, She took me half the way there, now.
   She was a day tripper, One way ticket, yeah;
   It took me so long to find out and I found out.

3. Tried to please her, She only played one night stands.
   Tried to please her, She only played one night stands, now.
   She was a day tripper, Sunday driver, yeah;
   It took me so long to find out and I found out.

Blackbird

Words & Music by John Lennon & Paul McCartney

Slow Folk Ballad

Black - bird sing - ing in the dead of night,
Take these bro - ken wings and learn to fly. All your life, ___
You were on - ly wait - ing for this mo - ment to a -
rise. Black - bird sing - ing in the dead of night,

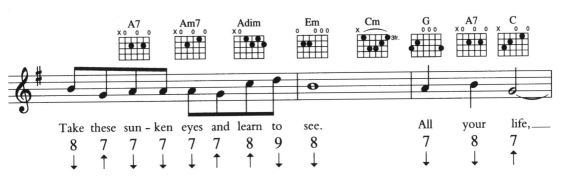

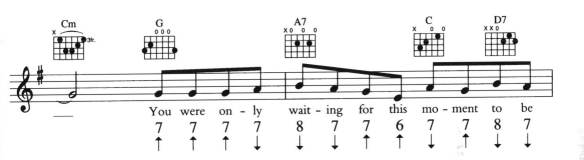

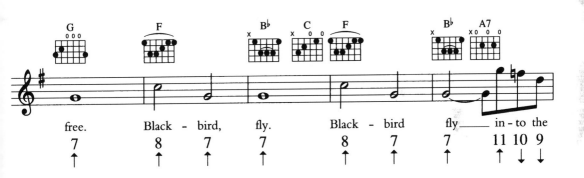

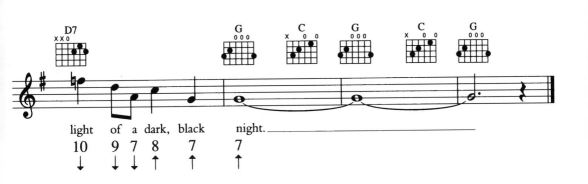

Ticket To Ride

Words & Music by John Lennon & Paul McCartney

I
1. think I'm gon - na be sad,___ I think it's to-
2. said that liv - ing with me___ is bring - ing her

5 6 7 7 7 6 5   7 7 7 7

day. Yeh! The girl that's dri - ving me mad___ Is go - ing a -
down. Yeh! For she would nev - er be free___ When I was a -

8 7 8 9 9 8 8 8 7   7 7 7 7

way.___ She's got a tick - et to ride,___
round.___ She's got a tick - et to ride,___

8   7 8 7 8 8 8 9

She's got a tick - et to ri - hi - hide._ She's got a tick - et to ride, but she don't
She's got a tick - et to ri - hi - hide._ She's got a tick - et to ride, but she don't

7 8 7 8 8 8 9 8 7   7 8 7 8 8 8 9 8 8 8

Norwegian Wood

Words & Music by John Lennon & Paul McCartney

She told me she worked in the morning and started to laugh.
I told her I didn't and crawled off to sleep in the bath.
And when I awoke, I was alone,
This bird had flown; So I lit a fire,
Isn't it good Norwegian Wood?

Lady Madonna

Words & Music by John Lennon & Paul McCartney

2. Lady Madonna, Lying on the bed,
Listen to the music playing in your head.
Tuesday afternoon is never ending,
Wednesday morning papers didn't come,
Thursday night your stocking needed mending.
See how they run.
Lady Madonna, Children at your feet,
Wonder how you manage to make ends meet.

23

I Saw Her Standing There

Words & Music by John Lennon & Paul McCartney

From Me To You

Words & Music by John Lennon & Paul McCartney

Get Back

Words & Music by John Lennon & Paul McCartney

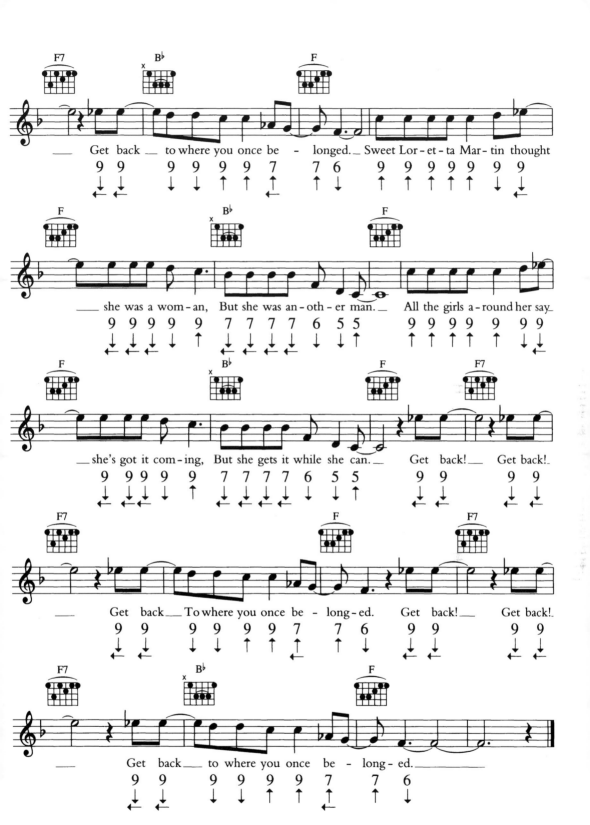

The Fool On The Hill

Words & Music by John Lennon & Paul McCartney

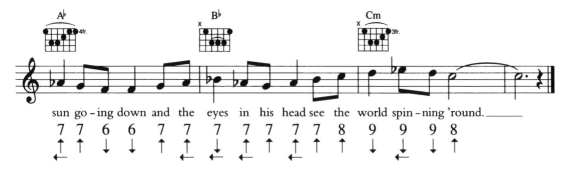

sun go-ing down and the eyes in his head see the world spin-ning 'round._____

7 7 6 6 7 7 7 7 7 7 7 8 9 9 9 8

2.   Well on the way, head in a cloud,
        The man of a thousand voices talking perfectly loud,
        But nobody ever hears him, or the sound he appears to make
        And he never seems to notice.
        But the fool on the hill sees the sun going down and the eyes in his head
        See the world spinning 'round.

3.   Day after day alone on a hill
        The man with the foolish grin is keeping perfectly still,
        And nobody seems to like him, they can tell what he wants to do
        And he never shows his feelings.
        But the fool on the hill sees the sun going down and the eyes in his head
        See the world spinning 'round.

4.   Day after day, alone on a hill
        The man with the foolish grin is keeping perfectly still.
        He never listens to them, he knows that they're the fools.
        They don't like him.
        But the fool on the hill sees the sun going down and the eyes in his head
        See the world spinning 'round.

Eleanor Rigby

Words & Music by John Lennon & Paul McCartney

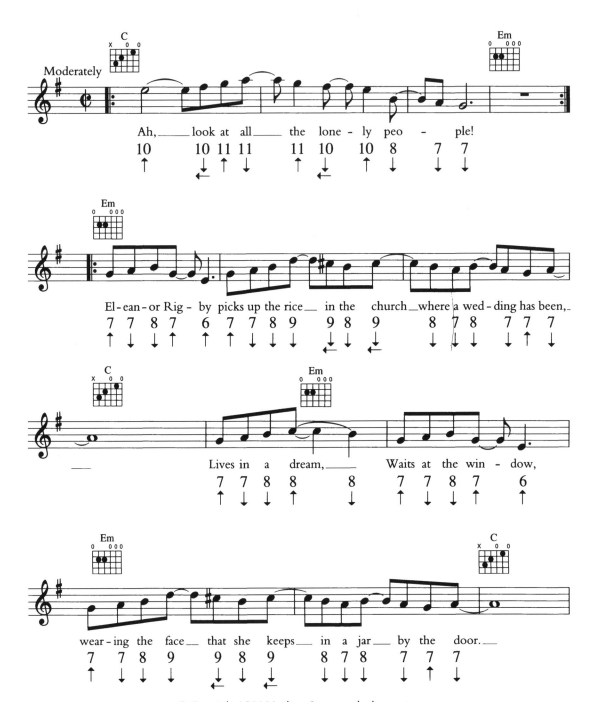

2.   Father McKenzie, writing the words of a sermon that no one will hear.
No one comes near. Look at him working, darning his socks in the night
When there's nobody there. What does he care?
All the lonely people, where do they all come from?
All the lonely people, where do they all belong?

3.   Eleanor Rigby died in the church and was buried along with her name.
Nobody came. Father McKenzie wiping the dirt from his hands as he walks
      from the grave no one was saved.
All the lonely people, where do they all come from?
All the lonely people, where do they all belong?

Can't Buy Me Love

Words & Music by John Lennon & Paul McCartney

I'll 1. buy you a dia-mond ring, ___ my friend,_ If it makes you feel al-right._
2. give you ___ all I've got ___ to give,_ If you say you love me, too._

5 8 8 8 7 7 7 6 6 6 5 6 5 5 6 6

___ I'll get you an-y-thing, ___ my friend,_ If it makes you feel al-right,_
___ I may not have a lot ___ to give, But what I've got I'll give to you,_

6 8 8 7 7 7 6 6 6 6 5 6 5 5 6 6

___ For I don't care too much for mon-ey, For mon-ey can't buy me love._ ___ I'll
___ For I don't care too much for mon-ey, For mon-ey can't buy me love.

6 8 8 8 8 7 7 7 7 5 8 8 8 7 7 6 5

1.

2.

Can't buy me love,___ Ev'-ry-bod-y tells me so._

6 7 8 8 7 7 7 7 6 7 6 6

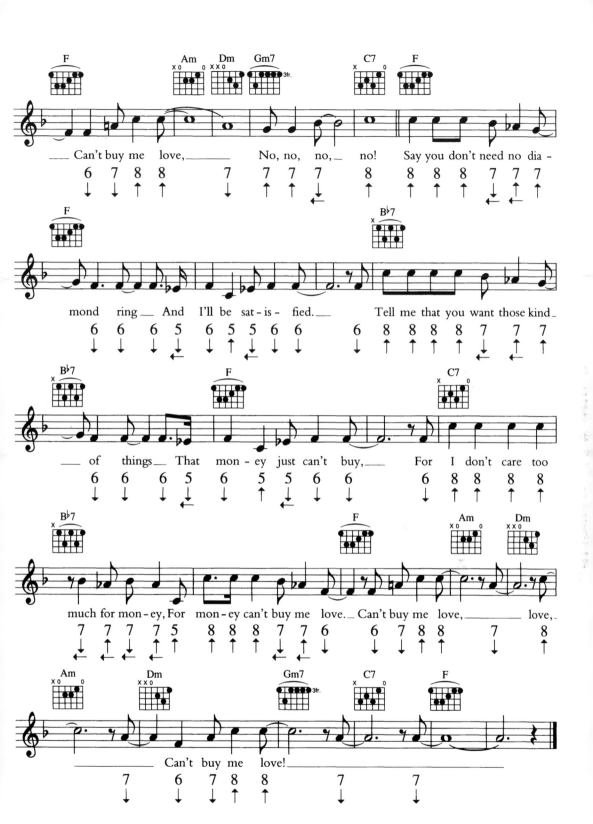

Hey Jude

Words & Music by John Lennon & Paul McCartney

Paperback Writer

Words & Music by John Lennon & Paul McCartney

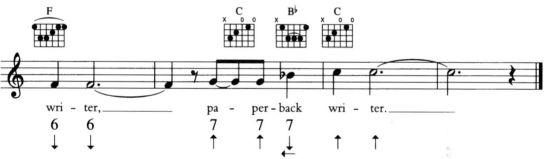

3. It's a thousand pages, give or take a few,
I'll be writing more in a week or two.
I can make it longer if you like the style,
I can change it 'round and I want to be a
paperback writer. Paperback writer.

4. If you really like it you can have the rights,
It could make a million for you over night.
If you must return it you can send it here,
But I need a break and I want to be a
paperback writer. Paperback writer.

Penny Lane

Words & Music by John Lennon & Paul McCartney

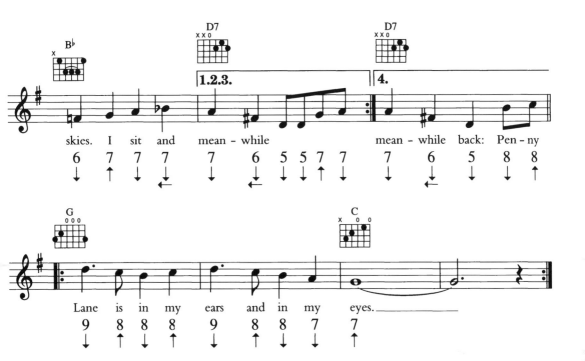

skies. I sit and mean – while mean – while back: Pen – ny
6 7 7 7 7 6 5 5 7 7 7 6 5 8 8

Lane is in my ears and in my eyes.
9 8 8 8 9 8 8 7 7

2. On the corner is a banker with a motor car.
   The little children laugh at him behind his back.
   And the banker never wears a "mac" in the pouring rain, very strange.
   Penny Lane is in my ears and in my eyes.
   There beneath the blue suburban skies I sit and meanwhile

3. Back in Penny Lane: there is a fireman with an hour glass.
   And in his pocket is a portrait of the Queen.
   He likes to keep his fire engine clean, it's a clean machine.
   Penny Lane is in my ears and in my eyes.
   Full of fish and finger pies in summer meanwhile

4. Back in Penny Lane: the barber shaves another customer.
   We see the banker sitting waiting for a trim.
   And then the fireman rushes in from the pouring rain, very strange.
   Penny Lane is in my ears and in my eyes.
   There beneath the blue suburban skies. I sit and meanwhile back:
   Penny Lane is in my ears and in my eyes.
   There beneath the blue suburban skies.

Carry That Weight

Words & Music by John Lennon & Paul McCartney

And I Love Her

Words & Music by John Lennon & Paul McCartney

Eight Days A Week

Words & Music by John Lennon & Paul McCartney

1.Ooh I need your love babe, guess you know it's true.
2. Love you ev' - ry day girl, al - ways on my mind.

Hope you need my love babe, Just like I need you..
One thing I can say girl, love you all the time.

Hold me,— love me,— hold me,—
Hold me,— love me,— hold me,—

love me.— Ain't got noth - in' but love babe,— Eight days a
love me.— Ain't got noth - in' but love girl,— Eight days a

week._____ Eight days a week I
week._____

9 9 7   9   9   9 9   7

love_____ you,_____ Eight days a

8 7 8 7   8 7 7   9   9   9

D.C. al fine

week is not e - nough to show I care:__

9   7 8 7 8 7   8 8 9

4. Love you ev' - ry day girl, al - ways on my mind.__

9 9 7 8   8   7   7 7 9 9 9

___ One thing I can say girl,

9 9 7 8   8   7

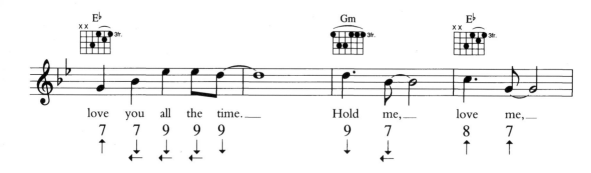

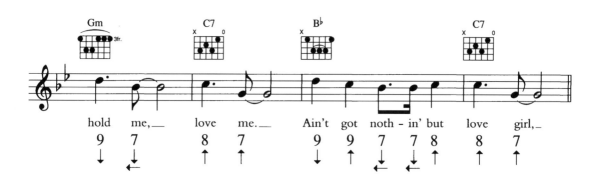

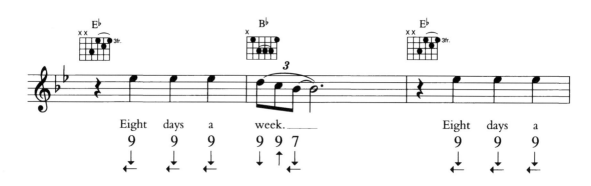

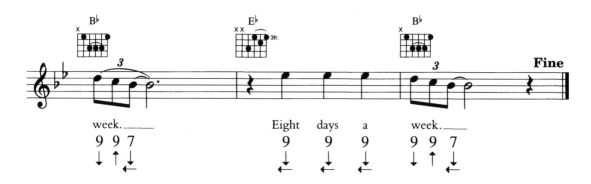

03/16(196720)